The WILD Thornberrys™

ANIMAL RIDDLES

ISBN 0-439-28551-8

12 11 10 9 8 7 6 5 4 3 2 1   1 2 3 4 5 6/0

Printed in the U.S.A.

First Scholastic printing, March 2001

ANIMAL RIDDLES

BY DAVID LEWMAN

SCHOLASTIC INC.

New York Toronto London Auckland Sydney
Mexico City New Delhi Hong Kong

Hi! I'm Eliza Thornberry and I travel all over the world with my family. My dad hosts a nature show, and my mom films it! But no one knows that I can talk to animals—or that I know lots of animal riddles!

You do?

Yeah, like this one: Why does Darwin sleep so much?

Um, because he's exhausted from all the adventures you drag him into?

No, because he needs his *chimpanzzz's!*

I hope **all** the riddles are not about me!

What's big and gray and
has a long sticky tongue?

An eleph-anteater.

What's big and gray and
never takes showers?

A smellephant.

How is a big elephant like a
tall tree?

They both have long
trunks.

What do elephants wear to
weddings?

Tush-sedos.

Why did the pianist touch the elephant's tusks?

He wanted to tickle the ivories.

What do mother apes sing
to their babies?

Gorillabyes.

What kind of fruit do
gorillas like best?

Ape-ricots.

When do gorillas play tricks
on each other?

Ape-ril Fool's Day!

How do you keep track of
gorilla songs?

With an ape recorder.

What's the most common gorilla name?

Harry.

When lions move to town,
where do they live?

Mane Street.

When is a lion like a fire?

When it's roaring.

Why did the chicken cross the lions?

To get to the other pride.

Why did the chicken cross the beach?

To get to the other tide.

What has bumps on its face and is always nervous?

A worry-warthog.

What do you call a crocodile that's almost grown up?

A teeth-ager.

What do you call a
porpoise that likes to
putt?

A golfin' dolphin.

What do you get when you
cross a bird with an ape?

A chickpanzee.

What's it called when a tortoise blocks the sun?

A turtle eclipse.

Why did Eliza bring a turtle to school?

For slow-and-shell.

Why did the turtle go to Philadelphia?

To see the Liberty Shell.

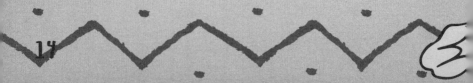

How do you start a turtle race?

"Ready, set, slow!"

What do you get when you cross a wild boar and a turtle?

A snortoise.

What do you get when you cross a wild boar and a lizard?

A piguana.

Where do wild pigs buy all their things?

From boar-to-boar salesmen.

Which bird is the greatest artist?

Leonardo da Finchy.

Which seabird has the cleanest teeth?

The albafloss.

What has a bald head, long wings, and a pot of gold?

The leprecondor.

Where do big, bald California birds like to live?

In condorminiums.

19

Why did the bat join the circus?

He wanted to be an acrobat.

Why did the magician train
the rodent not to gnaw?

He wanted to pull a habit
out of a rat.

What kind of bats do you
find in a bell tower?

Dingbats.

What has a horn, is very heavy, and will try anything once?

The why-notceros.

What has a horn, is very heavy, and goes great with pastrami?

The rye-noceros.

Why do rhinos belong to lots of clubs?

They just keep horning in.

What has a horn, is very heavy, and stands in the corner at parties?

The shy-nocerous.

Which bug is best at catching rhinos?

The hornet.

What do you call someone who's crazy about female deer?

A doe nut.

How do baby deer call each other?

They use the tell-a-fawn.

What do you call a funny male deer?

A comic buck.

What do you get when you cross a melon and a caribou?

A rind-deer.

What do you
call a blushing
male deer?

A coloring buck.

Where can you win the world's tallest animal?

In a gi-raffle.

What's a giraffe's favorite fruit?

Neck-tarines.

Why do giraffes take so many chances?

They like sticking their necks out.

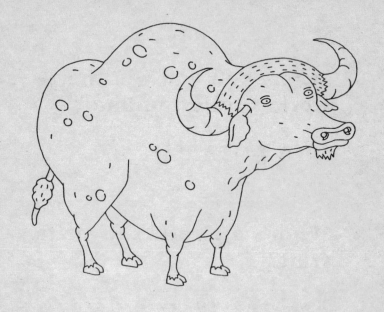

What's big and hairy and crazy?

The buffaloco.

What's Superfish's secret identity?

Shark Kent.

When is an Australian dog like a bell?

When it's a dingo.

What is graceful, lives in Africa, and wears little pointy shoes?

The gazelf.

Where do hyenas like to race?

On a laugh track.

Why did the Thornberrys go to Australia?

To spend some koalaty time together.

Which bird never tells the truth?

The lyrebird.

If lizards had their own country, what would it be called?

Geckoslovakia.

How do you find leopards at night?

With a spotlight.

Who's every tiger's favorite actress?

Meryl Stripe

Which big, flightless bird
lives at the North Pole?

The frostrich.

Which big, flightless bird
is always tired?

The exhaustrich.

What does a
hungry ostrich
do at lunchtime?

Buries his head
in a sandwich.

Which big, flightless bird always tells on you?

The osnitch.

What do you get when you cross a big snake with a big California bird?

An anacondor.

Why did the vultures keep going back to the bad restaurant?

The food was rotten.

What did the rat say to the mouse?

"Oh, go jump in the snake."

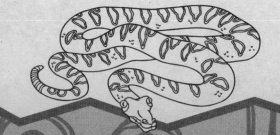

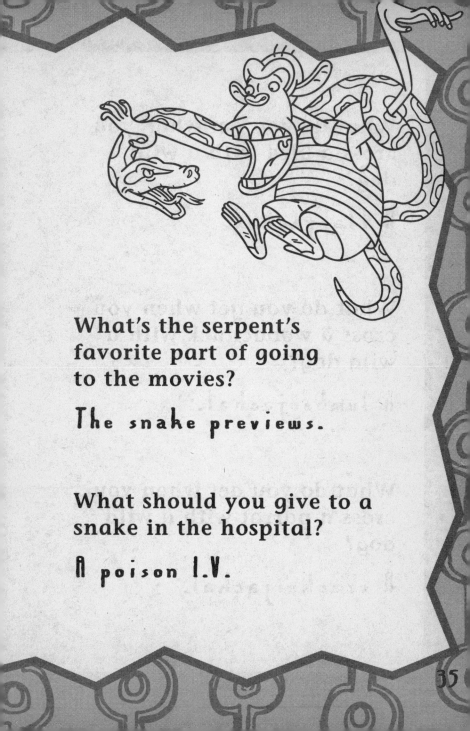

What's the serpent's
favorite part of going
to the movies?

The snake previews.

What should you give to a
snake in the hospital?

A poison I.V.

What do you get when you cross a bird with a wild dog?

A flapjackal.

What do you get when you cross a woodchuck with a wild dog?

A lumberjackal.

What do you get when you cross a parrot with a wild dog?

A crackerjackal.

Which animal is best at reciting the alphabet?

The XYZebra.

What lives in Australia,
hops, and makes a great
drum?

A congaroo.

What lives in Australia,
hops, and crows at dawn?

A kangarooster.

What are kangaroos like
when they first wake up?

Pouchy.

What do you call a
telegram from a kangaroo?

A jumper cable.

Why don't kangaroos ever use doors?

They love to go window-hopping.

What do kangaroos wear to the office?

Jumpsuits.

What did the mongoose fix for dinner?

Snake 'n' Bake.

What do snakes like to drink?

Cobra cola.

Which snake goes great with ice cream?

The apple python.

What do young male whales
do for fun?

They join the Boy Spouts.

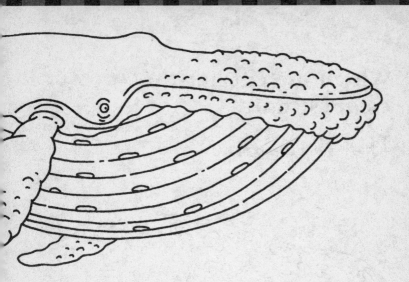

What happens to fish who commit crimes?

They get thrown in whale.

Which big cat has the
cleanest hair?

The shampuma.

What's it called when you
act like a crazy, big cat?

Livin' la cheetah loca.

What do skunks look for in a leader?

The ability to stink on your feet.

Why did the small bird fly upside down?

Because she was a little cuckoo.

Who starts to blow your house down, but quickly loses interest?

The big bored wolf.

Why did the family of wolves climb on the elephant?

They wanted to be a back pack.

Why are donkeys honest?

Because crime doesn't bray.

Which lizard likes to wear Japanese gowns?

The Kimono dragon.

What kind of jokes do birds
like best?

Flock-flock jokes!